This diary belongs to

First published in 2015
by Faber & Faber
Bloomsbury House
74–77 Great Russell Street
London WC1B 3DA

Designed and typeset by Faber & Faber Ltd

Printed in China by C&C Offset Printing Co. Ltd

Clauses in the Banking and Financial Dealings Act allow the government
to alter dates at short notice

A CIP record for this book is available from the British Library

ISBN 978–0–571–31807–0 (dark blue cover edition)
ISBN 978–0–571–31808–7 (pale blue cover edition)
ISBN 978–0–571–32618–1 (special edition with *The North Ship* cover,
available exclusively from www.faber.co.uk)

The colours of this year's diary are taken from the jacket design by
Berthold Wolpe for the 1966 edition of Philip Larkin's collection,
The North Ship.

Wendy Cope
Family Values

Walter
de la Mare
Selected
Poems
Edited by Matthew Sweeney

ff Poetry

Lawrence
Durrell
Selected
Poems
Edited by Peter Porter

ff Poetry

James
Fenton
Yellow
Tulips
Poems 1968–2011

ff Poetry

David
Harsent
Night

Michael
Hofmann
Selected
Poems

ff

Mick Imlah
The Lost
Leader

ff

Emma Jones
The Striped
World

Paul
Muldoon
Maggot

Daljit Nagra
Tippoo Sultan's
Incredible
White-Man-
Eating Tiger
Toy-Machine!!!

ff Poetry

Alice
Oswald
Memorial

ff Poetry

Don
Paterson
Rain

ff

Chapcott
Of
Mutability

Stephen
Spender
New
Collected
Poems

ff Poetry

Derek
Walcott
White
Egrets

ff Poetry

Hugo
Williams
West End
Final

ff

Faber
& Faber
Poetry
Diary
2016

JANUARY

M	T	W	T	F	S	S
28	29	30	31	1	2	3
4	5	6	7	8	9	10
11	12	13	14	15	16	17
18	19	20	21	22	23	24
25	26	27	28	29	30	31
1	2	3	4	5	6	7

FEBRUARY

M	T	W	T	F	S	S
25	26	27	28	29	30	31
1	2	3	4	5	6	7
8	9	10	11	12	13	14
15	16	17	18	19	20	21
22	23	24	25	26	27	28
29	1	2	3	4	5	6

MARCH

M	T	W	T	F	S	S
29	1	2	3	4	5	6
7	8	9	10	11	12	13
14	15	16	17	18	19	20
21	22	23	24	25	26	27
28	29	30	31	1	2	3
4	5	6	7	8	9	10

APRIL

M	T	W	T	F	S	S
28	29	30	31	1	2	3
4	5	6	7	8	9	10
11	12	13	14	15	16	17
18	19	20	21	22	23	24
25	26	27	28	29	30	1
2	3	4	5	6	7	8

MAY

M	T	W	T	F	S	S
25	26	27	28	29	30	1
2	3	4	5	6	7	8
9	10	11	12	13	14	15
16	17	18	19	20	21	22
23	24	25	26	27	28	29
30	31	1	2	3	4	5

JUNE

M	T	W	T	F	S	S
30	31	1	2	3	4	5
6	7	8	9	10	11	12
13	14	15	16	17	18	19
20	21	22	23	24	25	26
27	28	29	30	1	2	3
4	5	6	7	8	9	10

JULY

M	T	W	T	F	S	S
27	28	29	30	1	2	3
4	5	6	7	8	9	10
11	12	13	14	15	16	17
18	19	20	21	22	23	24
25	26	27	28	29	30	31
1	2	3	4	5	6	7

AUGUST

M	T	W	T	F	S	S
1	2	3	4	5	6	7
8	9	10	11	12	13	14
15	16	17	18	19	20	21
22	23	24	25	26	27	28
29	30	31	1	2	3	4
5	6	7	8	9	10	11

SEPTEMBER

M	T	W	T	F	S	S
29	30	31	1	2	3	4
5	6	7	8	9	10	11
12	13	14	15	16	17	18
19	20	21	22	23	24	25
26	27	28	29	30	1	2
3	4	5	6	7	8	9

OCTOBER

M	T	W	T	F	S	S
26	27	28	29	30	1	2
3	4	5	6	7	8	9
10	11	12	13	14	15	16
17	18	19	20	21	22	23
24	25	26	27	28	29	30
31	1	2	3	4	5	6

NOVEMBER

M	T	W	T	F	S	S
31	1	2	3	4	5	6
7	8	9	10	11	12	13
14	15	16	17	18	19	20
21	22	23	24	25	26	27
28	29	30	1	2	3	4
5	6	7	8	9	10	11

DECEMBER

M	T	W	T	F	S	S
28	29	30	1	2	3	4
5	6	7	8	9	10	11
12	13	14	15	16	17	18
19	20	21	22	23	24	25
26	27	28	29	30	31	1
2	3	4	5	6	7	8

2015

JANUARY
M	T	W	T	F	S	S
29	30	31	1	2	3	4
5	6	7	8	9	10	11
12	13	14	15	16	17	18
19	20	21	22	23	24	25
26	27	28	29	30	31	1
2	3	4	5	6	7	8

FEBRUARY
M	T	W	T	F	S	S
26	27	28	29	30	31	1
2	3	4	5	6	7	8
9	10	11	12	13	14	15
16	17	18	19	20	21	22
23	24	25	26	27	28	1
2	3	4	5	6	7	8

MARCH
M	T	W	T	F	S	S
23	24	25	26	27	28	1
2	3	4	5	6	7	8
9	10	11	12	13	14	15
16	17	18	19	20	21	22
23	24	25	26	27	28	29
30	31	1	2	3	4	5

APRIL
M	T	W	T	F	S	S
30	31	1	2	3	4	5
6	7	8	9	10	11	12
13	14	15	16	17	18	19
20	21	22	23	24	25	26
27	28	29	30	1	2	3
4	5	6	7	8	9	10

MAY
M	T	W	T	F	S	S
27	28	29	30	1	2	3
4	5	6	7	8	9	10
11	12	13	14	15	16	17
18	19	20	21	22	23	24
25	26	27	28	29	30	31
1	2	3	4	5	6	7

JUNE
M	T	W	T	F	S	S
1	2	3	4	5	6	7
8	9	10	11	12	13	14
15	16	17	18	19	20	21
22	23	24	25	26	27	28
29	30	1	2	3	4	5
6	7	8	9	10	11	12

JULY
M	T	W	T	F	S	S
29	30	1	2	3	4	5
6	7	8	9	10	11	12
13	14	15	16	17	18	19
20	21	22	23	24	25	26
27	28	29	30	31	1	2
3	4	5	6	7	8	9

AUGUST
M	T	W	T	F	S	S
27	28	29	30	31	1	2
3	4	5	6	7	8	9
10	11	12	13	14	15	16
17	18	19	20	21	22	23
24	25	26	27	28	29	30
31	1	2	3	4	5	6

SEPTEMBER
M	T	W	T	F	S	S
31	1	2	3	4	5	6
7	8	9	10	11	12	13
14	15	16	17	18	19	20
21	22	23	24	25	26	27
28	29	30	1	2	3	4
5	6	7	8	9	10	11

OCTOBER
M	T	W	T	F	S	S
28	29	30	1	2	3	4
5	6	7	8	9	10	11
12	13	14	15	16	17	18
19	20	21	22	23	24	25
26	27	28	29	30	31	1
2	3	4	5	6	7	8

NOVEMBER
M	T	W	T	F	S	S
26	27	28	29	30	31	1
2	3	4	5	6	7	8
9	10	11	12	13	14	15
16	17	18	19	20	21	22
23	24	25	26	27	28	29
30	1	2	3	4	5	6

DECEMBER
M	T	W	T	F	S	S
30	1	2	3	4	5	6
7	8	9	10	11	12	13
14	15	16	17	18	19	20
21	22	23	24	25	26	27
28	29	30	31	1	2	3
4	5	6	7	8	9	10

2017

JANUARY
M	T	W	T	F	S	S
26	27	28	29	30	31	1
2	3	4	5	6	7	8
9	10	11	12	13	14	15
16	17	18	19	20	21	22
23	24	25	26	27	28	29
30	31	1	2	3	4	5

FEBRUARY
M	T	W	T	F	S	S
30	31	1	2	3	4	5
6	7	8	9	10	11	12
13	14	15	16	17	18	19
20	21	22	23	24	25	26
27	28	1	2	3	4	5
6	7	8	9	10	11	12

MARCH
M	T	W	T	F	S	S
27	28	1	2	3	4	5
6	7	8	9	10	11	12
13	14	15	16	17	18	19
20	21	22	23	24	25	26
27	28	29	30	31	1	2
3	4	5	6	7	8	9

APRIL
M	T	W	T	F	S	S
27	28	29	30	31	1	2
3	4	5	6	7	8	9
10	11	12	13	14	15	16
17	18	19	20	21	22	23
24	25	26	27	28	29	30
1	2	3	4	5	6	7

MAY
M	T	W	T	F	S	S
1	2	3	4	5	6	7
8	9	10	11	12	13	14
15	16	17	18	19	20	21
22	23	24	25	26	27	28
29	30	31	1	2	3	4
5	6	7	8	9	10	11

JUNE
M	T	W	T	F	S	S
29	30	31	1	2	3	4
5	6	7	8	9	10	11
12	13	14	15	16	17	18
19	20	21	22	23	24	25
26	27	28	29	30	1	2
3	4	5	6	7	8	9

JULY
M	T	W	T	F	S	S
26	27	28	29	30	1	2
3	4	5	6	7	8	9
10	11	12	13	14	15	16
17	18	19	20	21	22	23
24	25	26	27	28	29	30
31	1	2	3	4	5	6

AUGUST
M	T	W	T	F	S	S
31	1	2	3	4	5	6
7	8	9	10	11	12	13
14	15	16	17	18	19	20
21	22	23	24	25	26	27
28	29	30	31	1	2	3
4	5	6	7	8	9	10

SEPTEMBER
M	T	W	T	F	S	S
28	29	30	31	1	2	3
4	5	6	7	8	9	10
11	12	13	14	15	16	17
18	19	20	21	22	23	24
25	26	27	28	29	30	1
2	3	4	5	6	7	8

OCTOBER
M	T	W	T	F	S	S
25	26	27	28	29	30	1
2	3	4	5	6	7	8
9	10	11	12	13	14	15
16	17	18	19	20	21	22
23	24	25	26	27	28	29
30	31	1	2	3	4	5

NOVEMBER
M	T	W	T	F	S	S
30	31	1	2	3	4	5
6	7	8	9	10	11	12
13	14	15	16	17	18	19
20	21	22	23	24	25	26
27	28	29	30	1	2	3
4	5	6	7	8	9	10

DECEMBER
M	T	W	T	F	S	S
27	28	29	30	1	2	3
4	5	6	7	8	9	10
11	12	13	14	15	16	17
18	19	20	21	22	23	24
25	26	27	28	29	30	31
1	2	3	4	5	6	7

77 DREAM SONGS

John Berryman

28 Monday

---

29 Tuesday

---

30 Wednesday

---

31 Thursday   NEW YEAR'S EVE

---

1 Friday   NEW YEAR'S DAY (UK, IRL, AUS, ZA, NZ)

---

2 Saturday   NEW YEAR'S HOLIDAY   3 Sunday
              (SCT)

The Garden of Love

I went to the Garden of Love.
And saw what I never had seen:
A Chapel was built in the midst,
Where I used to play on the green.

And the gates of this Chapel were shut,
And Thou shalt not. writ over the door;
So I turn'd to the Garden of Love,
That so many sweet flowers bore.

And I saw it was filled with graves,
And tomb-stones where flowers should be:
And Priests in black gowns, were walking their rounds,
And binding with briars, my joys & desires.

POET TO POET — *William Blake: Poems selected by James Fenton*

4 Monday DAY AFTER NEW YEAR'S DAY (NZ)

5 Tuesday

6 Wednesday

7 Thursday

8 Friday

9 Saturday   10 Sunday

From 'Glanmore Sonnets'

VII

Dogger, Rockall, Malin, Irish Sea:
Green, swift upsurges, North Atlantic flux
Conjured by that strong gale-warning voice
Collapse into a sibilant penumbra,
Midnight and closedown. Sirens of the tundra,
Of eel-road, seal-road, keel-road, whale-road, raise
Their wind-compounded keen behind the baize
And drive the trawlers to the lee of Wicklow.
L'Etoile, Le Guillemot, La Belle Hélène
Nursed their bright names this morning in the bay
That toiled like mortar. It was marvellous
And actual, I said out loud, 'A haven,'
The word deepening, clearing, like the sky
Elsewhere on Minches, Cromarty, The Faroes.

11   Monday

12   Tuesday

13   Wednesday

14   Thursday

15   Friday

16   Saturday   17   Sunday

'Surprised by joy – impatient as the Wind'

Surprised by joy – impatient as the Wind
I turned to share the transport – Oh! with whom
But Thee, deep buried in the silent tomb,
That spot which no vicissitude can find?
Love, faithful love, recalled thee to my mind –
But how could I forget thee? Through what power,
Even for the least division of an hour,
Have I been so beguiled as to be blind
To my most grievous loss! – That thought's return
Was the worst pang that sorrow ever bore,
Save one, one only, when I stood forlorn,
Knowing my heart's best treasure was no more;
That neither present time, nor years unborn
Could to my sight that heavenly face restore.

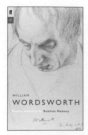

POET TO POET – *William Wordsworth: Poems selected by Seamus Heaney*

18 Monday

19 Tuesday

20 Wednesday

21 Thursday

22 Friday

23 Saturday   24 Sunday

Bonnie Peg

As I cam in by our gate-end,
    As day was waxen weary,
O wha cam tripping down the street
    But bonnie Peg, my dearie!

Her air sae sweet, and shape complete,
    Wi' nae proportion wanting,
The queen of love did never move
    Wi' motion mair enchanting.

Wi' linked hands we took the sands
    Adown yon winding river;
And, oh! that hour, and broomy bower,
    Can I forget it ever!

POET TO POET – *Robert Burns: Poems selected by Don Paterson*

25 Monday   BURNS NIGHT (SCT)

26 Tuesday   AUSTRALIA DAY (AUS)

27 Wednesday

28 Thursday

29 Friday

30 Saturday   31 Sunday

e.e. cummings

selected poems

1923-1958

Faber paper covered editions

1 Monday

2 Tuesday

3 Wednesday

4 Thursday

5 Friday

6 Saturday   WAITANGI DAY (NZ)   7 Sunday

'After great pain, a formal feeling comes'

After great pain, a formal feeling comes –
The Nerves sit ceremonious, like Tombs –
The stiff Heart questions was it He, that bore,
And Yesterday, or Centuries before?

The Feet, mechanical, go round –
Of Ground, or Air, or Ought –
A Wooden way
Regardless grown,
A Quartz contentment, like a stone –

This is the Hour of Lead –
Remembered, if outlived,
As Freezing persons, recollect the Snow –
First – Chill – then Stupor – then the letting go

POET TO POET – *Emily Dickinson: Poems selected by Ted Hughes*

8 Monday WAITANGI DAY HOLIDAY (NZ)

9 Tuesday SHROVE TUESDAY

10 Wednesday

11 Thursday

12 Friday

13 Saturday

14 Sunday VALENTINE'S DAY

Morning Song

Love set you going like a fat gold watch.
The midwife slapped your footsoles, and your bald cry
Took its place among the elements.

Our voices echo, magnifying your arrival. New statue.
In a drafty museum, your nakedness
Shadows our safety. We stand round blankly as walls.

I'm no more your mother
Than the cloud that distills a mirror to reflect its own slow
Effacement at the wind's hand.

All night your moth-breath
Flickers among the flat pink roses. I wake to listen:
A far sea moves in my ear.

One cry, and I stumble from bed, cow-heavy and floral
In my Victorian nightgown.
Your mouth opens clean as a cat's. The window square

Whitens and swallows its dull stars. And now you try
Your handful of notes;
The clear vowels rise like balloons.

15 Monday

16 Tuesday

17 Wednesday

18 Thursday

19 Friday

20 Saturday   21 Sunday

The long small room

The long small room that showed willows in the west
Narrowed up to the end the fireplace filled,
Although not wide. I liked it. No one guessed
What need or accident made them so build.

Only the moon, the mouse and the sparrow peeped
In from the ivy round the casement thick.
Of all they saw and heard there they shall keep
The tale for the old ivy and older brick.

When I look back I am like moon, sparrow and mouse
That witnessed what they could never understand
Or alter or prevent in the dark house.
One thing remains the same – this my right hand

Crawling crab-like over the clean white page,
Resting awhile each morning on the pillow,
Then once more starting to crawl on towards age.
The hundred last leaves stream upon the willow.

22 Monday

23 Tuesday

24 Wednesday

25 Thursday

26 Friday

27 Saturday   28 Sunday

the
faber book
of
IRISH
VERSE

edited by
John Montague

29 Monday

1 Tuesday   ST DAVID'S DAY

2 Wednesday

3 Thursday

4 Friday

5 Saturday   6 Sunday

The Tomato Salad

was breathtaking. Sometime in the late 1990s
the Californian sun ripened a crop of tomatoes
to such a pitch you could hear them screaming.
Did I mention this was in California? There was
corn on the cob. She was English and her heart
almost stopped when her aunt served her a bowl
of red and yellow tomatoes so spectacular she would
never get over them. I can only imagine the perfectly
suspended seeds, the things a cut tomato knows
about light, or in what fresh voice of sweet and tart
those tomatoes spoke when they told my dearest
friend, 'Yosçi yosçi lom boca sá tutty foo twa
tamata,' in the language of all sun-ripened fruits.

7 Monday

8 Tuesday

9 Wednesday

10 Thursday

11 Friday

12 Saturday   13 Sunday

The Flea

Marke but this flea, and marke in this,
How little that which thou deny'st me is;
It suck'd me first, and now sucks thee,
And in this flea, our two bloods mingled bee;
Thou know'st that this cannot be said
A sinne, nor shame, nor losse of maidenhead,
    Yet this enjoyes before it wooe,
      And pamper'd swells with one blood made of two,
      And this, alas, is more then wee would doe.

Oh stay, three lives in one flea spare,
Where wee almost, yea more then maryed are,
This flea is you and I, and this
Our mariage bed, and mariage temple is;
Though parents grudge, and you, w'are met,
And cloysterd in these living walls of Jet.
    Though use make you apt to kill mee,
      Let not to that, selfe murder added bee,
      And sacrilege, three sinnes in killing three.

Cruell and sodaine, hast thou since
Purpled thy naile, in blood of innocence?
Wherein could this flea guilty bee,
Except in that drop which it suckt from thee?
Yet thou triumph'st, and saist that thou
Find'st not thy selfe, nor mee the weaker now;
    'Tis true, then learne how false, feares bee;
      Just so much honor, when thou yeeld'st to mee,
      Will wast, as this flea's death tooke life from thee.

POET TO POET — *John Donne: Poems selected by Paul Muldoon*

14 Monday

15 Tuesday

16 Wednesday

17 Thursday   ST PATRICK'S DAY (IRL, NI)

18 Friday

19 Saturday   20 Sunday

Heronkind

Whatever is desired
is grown toward:
a glimmer of fish
at the margins of rivers
and streams, or in marshes
triggers a longing –
a muted, persistent
itch in the newborn
heron which
she feels at the base of her
fledgling bill, a sense that will
persist until the optimal
fish-spearing length is reached.
From this point to
eternity her dreams
are crammed with fish
or the nervy, darting
shadows of fish.
How much less complex
life would be
without this feverish
dance between
the wanter and the wanted,
though the truth of it is
that without fish
all heronkind would
be stunted.

21 Monday   HUMAN RIGHTS DAY (ZA)

22 Tuesday

23 Wednesday

24 Thursday

25 Friday   GOOD FRIDAY (UK, IRL, AUS, ZA, NZ)

26 Saturday   EASTER SATURDAY (AUS) 27 Sunday   EASTER SUNDAY (UK, AUS, ZA)

Lawrence DURRELL

VEGA

and other POEMS

28 Monday   EASTER MONDAY (UK, IRL, CA, AUS, NZ) FAMILY DAY (ZA)

29 Tuesday

30 Wednesday

31 Thursday

1 Friday

2 Saturday   3 Sunday

Religion

If it were up to me
I would make use of sleep.
Going to church
would involve a flight of stairs
to a familiar bedroom,
where a broken alarm clock told the time.
The spreading of sheets,
the turning down of blankets,
would be followed by the drawing of curtains
in broad daylight,
the ritual of undressing.

Members of my religion
would be encouraged to sleep in
on Monday mornings
and any other morning they felt like it,
with no questions asked.
Sleep notes would be provided.
Couples would be authorised
to pull the covers over their heads
and spend their days tucked up
in cosy confessionals,
where all their sins would be forgiven.

4 Monday

5 Tuesday

6 Wednesday

7 Thursday

8 Friday

9 Saturday   10 Sunday

Teazles

Out in the vacant lot to gather weeds
I found these teazles – their ovoid heads
delicately armoured with crowns of thorns.
Arthur, from whom I haven't heard a word
in thirty years, who must be ninety if
he's a day, told me they were used to raise
the nap on the green felt of billiards tables
and, since Roman times, for combing woollen stuff.
He also said their seeds were caviar
to the goldfinch. And then I lost the knife
he'd lent me to cut some – the loss of which
was the cause of grief. In honour of gruff Arthur
I shake the seeds out in our small green patch
and stick the spiky seed heads in a jar.

11 Monday

12 Tuesday

13 Wednesday

14 Thursday

15 Friday

16 Saturday 17 Sunday

Because I Liked You

Because I liked you better
    Than suits a man to say,
It irked you, and I promised
    To throw the thought away.

To put the world between us
    We parted, stiff and dry;
'Good-bye,' said you, 'forget me.'
    'I will, no fear', said I.

If here, where clover whitens
    The dead man's knoll, you pass,
And no tall flower to meet you
    Starts in the trefoiled grass,

Halt by the headstone naming
    The heart no longer stirred,
And say the lad that loved you
    Was one that kept his word.

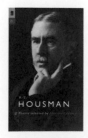

POET TO POET — *A. E. Housman: Poems selected by Alan Hollinghurst*

18 Monday

---

19 Tuesday

---

20 Wednesday

---

21 Thursday

---

22 Friday

---

23 Saturday ST GEORGE'S DAY   24 Sunday

Modern Love

It is summer, and we are in a house
That is not ours, sitting at a table
Enjoying minutes of a rented silence,
The upstairs people gone. The pigeons lull
To sleep the under-tens and invalids,
The tree shakes out its shadows to the grass,
The roses rove through the wilds of my neglect.
Our lives flap, and we have no hope of better
Happiness than this, not much to show for love
But how we are, or how this evening is,
Unpeopled, silent, and where we are alive
In domestic love, seemingly alone,
All other lives worn down to trees and sunlight,
Looking forward to a visit from the cat.

25 Monday   ANZAC DAY (AUS, NZ)

---

26 Tuesday

---

27 Wednesday   FREEDOM DAY (ZA)

---

28 Thursday

---

29 Friday

---

30 Saturday   1 Sunday   WORKERS' DAY (ZA)

Moly

THOM GUNN

2 Monday WORKERS' DAY HOLIDAY (ZA) EARLY MAY BANK HOLIDAY (UK)
MAY DAY (IRL)

3 Tuesday

4 Wednesday

5 Thursday

6 Friday

7 Saturday   8 Sunday

The Flower that Smiles Today

The flower that smiles today
    To-morrow dies;
All that we wish to stay
    Tempts and then flies.
What is this world's delight?
Lightning that mocks the night,
    Brief even as bright.

Virtue, how frail it is!
    Friendship how rare!
Love, how it sells poor bliss
    For proud despair!
But we, though soon they fall,
Survive their joy, and all
    Which ours we call.

Whilst skies are blue and bright,
    Whilst flowers are gay,
Whilst eyes that change ere night
    Make glad the day;
Whilst yet the calm hours creep,
Dream thou – and from thy sleep
    Then wake to weep.

POET TO POET – *Percy Bysshe Shelley: Poems selected by Fiona Sampson*

9 Monday

10 Tuesday

11 Wednesday

12 Thursday

13 Friday

14 Saturday   15 Sunday

If I Could Tell You

Time will say nothing but I told you so,
Time only knows the price we have to pay;
If I could tell you I would let you know.

If we should weep when clowns put on their show,
If we should stumble when musicians play,
Time will say nothing but I told you so.

There are no fortunes to be told, although,
Because I love you more than I can say,
If I could tell you I would let you know.

The winds must come from somewhere when they blow,
There must be reason why the leaves decay;
Time will say nothing but I told you so.

Perhaps the roses really want to grow,
The vision seriously intends to stay;
If I could tell you I would let you know.

Suppose the lions all get up and go,
And the brooks and soldiers run away;
Will Time say nothing but I told you so?
If I could tell you I would let you know.

16 Monday

17 Tuesday

18 Wednesday

19 Thursday

20 Friday

21 Saturday   22 Sunday

Sonnet 34

Why didst thou promise such a beauteous day,
And make me travel forth without my cloak,
To let base clouds o'ertake me in my way,
Hiding thy brav'ry in their rotten smoke?
'Tis not enough that through the cloud thou break,
To dry the rain on my storm-beaten face,
For no man well of such a salve can speak
That heals the wound, and cures not the disgrace;
Nor can thy shame give physic to my grief;
Though thou repent, yet I have still the loss;
The offender's sorrow lends but weak relief
To him that bears the strong offence's cross.
    Ah, but those tears are pearl which thy love sheds,
    And they are rich, and ransom all ill deeds.

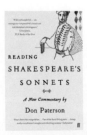

23 Monday

24 Tuesday

25 Wednesday

26 Thursday

27 Friday

28 Saturday   29 Sunday

Year of the Rabbit

there is no purer form of advertising
than writing a poem
that's what the monk told me
if I were a conceptual artist
I would make high-budget trailers
of john updike novels but no actual movie
the scene where angstrom drives towards
the end of his life down a street in the suburbs
lined with a type of tree he's never bothered
to identify and laden with white blossoms
reflecting slickly in the windscreen
I would fade in the music
as the old song was fading out
keeping the backing vocals at the same distance
kind of balancing the silence
the word RABBIT appears in 10-foot trebuchet

30 Monday   SPRING BANK HOLIDAY (UK)

31 Tuesday

1 Wednesday

2 Thursday

3 Friday

4 Saturday   5 Sunday

The Faber
BOOK OF
POPULAR
VERSE

edited with an Introduction by
Geoffrey Grigson

6 Monday   JUNE BANK HOLIDAY (IRL) QUEEN'S BIRTHDAY HOLIDAY (NZ)

7 Tuesday

8 Wednesday

9 Thursday

10 Friday

11 Saturday   12 Sunday

The Strand

White Tintoretto clouds beneath my naked feet,
This mirror of wet sand imputes a lasting mood
To island truancies; my steps repeat

Someone's who now has left such strands for good
Carrying his boots and paddling like a child,
A square black figure whom the horizon understood –

My father. Who for all his responsibly compiled
Account books of a devout, precise routine
Kept something in him solitary and wild,

So loved the western sea and no tree's green
Fulfilled him like these contours of Slievemore
Menaun and Croaghaun and the bogs between.

Sixty-odd years behind him and twelve before,
Eyeing the flange of steel in the turning belt of brine
It was sixteen years ago he walked this shore

And the mirror caught his shape which catches mine
But then as now the floor-mop of the foam
Blotted the bright reflections – and no sign

Remains of face or feet when visitors have gone home.

13 Monday

14 Tuesday

15 Wednesday

16 Thursday   YOUTH DAY (ZA)

17 Friday

18 Saturday   19 Sunday

Canute

They'll get it all wrong – pretty quickly, here,
from what I learn of tavern-talk and gossip;
they say I told the sea that it must stop
inching up shingle to my throne's four legs.
That was my point. I did, and it did not.

Imagine setting up a throne on shingle
to prove the king's a man like other men,
the waste of time spent ordering the grey
dead waters to obey my windswept voice.
It was a flat grey light in which I sat,
the sea curdling a small way out, then running
free at its last breath up the sliding pebbles,
gasping and falling back but always rising,
rising until it splashed my sandalled feet
and I'd had it with telling it to stop,
shaking my sceptre, telling it again.

I got up, gathered in my robe and left.
The disappointed flatterers didn't follow,
not straight away. The servants brought the throne.
No, being king confers no special powers.
And yet one wonders. Yes, of course one wonders.

20 Monday

21 Tuesday

22 Wednesday

23 Thursday

24 Friday

25 Saturday   26 Sunday

I Leave This at Your Ear

for Nessie Dunsmuir

I leave this at your ear for when you wake,
A creature in its abstract cage asleep.
Your dreams blindfold you by the light they make.

The owl called from the naked-woman tree
As I came down by the Kyle farm to hear
Your house silent by the speaking sea.

I have come late but I have come before
Later with slaked steps from stone to stone
To hope to find you listening for the door.

I stand in the ticking room. My dear, I take
A moth kiss from your breath. The shore gulls cry.
I leave this at your ear for when you wake.

27 Monday

28 Tuesday

29 Wednesday

30 Thursday

1 Friday

2 Saturday   3 Sunday

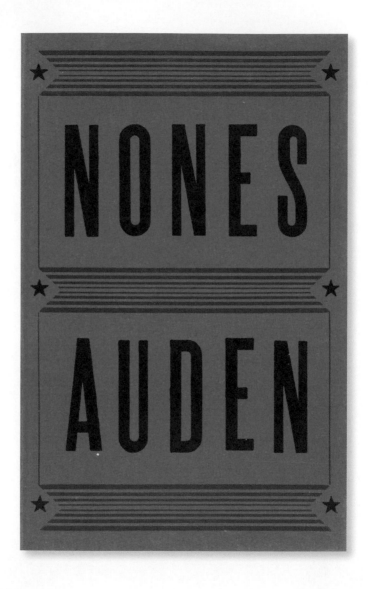

4 Monday

5 Tuesday

6 Wednesday

7 Thursday

8 Friday

9 Saturday   10 Sunday

The Day I Outlived My Father

Yet no one sent me flowers, or even
asked me out for a drink. If anything
it makes it worse, your early death, that
having now at last outlived you, I too
have broken ranks, lacking maybe
the imagination to follow you
in investigating that other, older world.

So I am in new territory from here on:
must blaze my own trail, read alone
the hoof tracks in the summer-powdered dust
and set a good face to the future:
at liberty at last like mad Arnaut
to cultivate the wind, to hunt the bull
on hare-back, to swim against the tide.

11 Monday

12 Tuesday BATTLE OF THE BOYNE HOLIDAY (NI)

13 Wednesday

14 Thursday

15 Friday

16 Saturday   17 Sunday

The Thunder Mutters

The thunder mutters louder and more loud;
With quicker motion hay folks ply the rake;
Ready to burst, slow sails the pitch black cloud
And all the gang a bigger haycock make
To sit beneath – the woodland winds awake
The drops so large. Wet all thro' in an hour
A tiny flood runs down the leaning rake
In the sweet hay, yet dry the hay folks cower,
And some beneath the waggon shun the shower.

POET TO POET – *John Clare: Poems selected by Paul Farley*

18 Monday

---

19 Tuesday

---

20 Wednesday

---

21 Thursday

---

22 Friday

---

23 Saturday   24 Sunday

'I stand alone, nor tho' my heart should break'

I stand alone, nor tho' my heart should break
Have I, to whom I may complain or speak.
Here I stand, a hopeless man and sad
Who hoped to have seen my Love, my Life.
And strange it were indeed, could I be glad
Remembering her, my Soul's betrothed wife
For in this World no creature, that has life,
Was e'er to me so gracious & so good
Her love was to my Heart, like the Heart-blood.

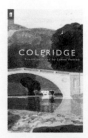

POET TO POET — *Samuel Taylor Coleridge: Poems selected by James Fenton*

25 Monday

26 Tuesday

27 Wednesday

28 Thursday

29 Friday

30 Saturday   31 Sunday

Hinterhof

Stay near to me and I'll stay near to you —
As near as you are dear to me will do,
    Near as the rainbow to the rain,
    The west wind to the windowpane,
As fire to the hearth, as dawn to dew.

Stay true to me and I'll stay true to you —
As true as you are new to me will do,
    New as the rainbow in the spray,
    Utterly new in every way,
New in the way that what you say is true.

Stay near to me, stay true to me. I'll stay
As near, as true to you as heart could pray.
    Heart never hoped that one might be
    Half of the things you are to me —
The dawn, the fire, the rainbow and the day.

1 Monday SUMMER BANK HOLIDAY (SCT, IRL)

2 Tuesday

3 Wednesday

4 Thursday

5 Friday

6 Saturday   7 Sunday

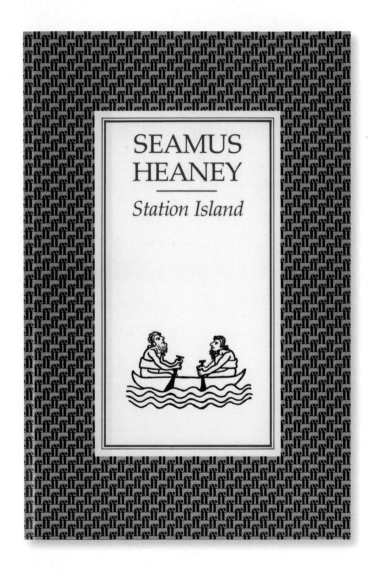

SEAMUS
HEANEY

Station Island

8 Monday

9 Tuesday NATIONAL WOMEN'S DAY HOLIDAY (ZA)

10 Wednesday

11 Thursday

12 Friday

13 Saturday   14 Sunday

At Galway Races

There where the course is,
Delight makes all of the one mind,
The riders upon the galloping horses,
The crowd that closes in behind:
We, too, had good attendance once,
Hearers and hearteners of the work;
Aye, horsemen for companions,
Before the merchant and the clerk
Breathed on the world with timid breath.
Sing on: somewhere at some new moon,
We'll learn that sleeping is not death,
Hearing the whole earth change its tune,
Its flesh being wild, and it again
Crying aloud as the racecourse is,
And we find hearteners among men
That ride upon horses.

POET TO POET — *W. B. Yeats: Poems selected by Seamus Heaney*

15 Monday

16 Tuesday

17 Wednesday

18 Thursday

19 Friday

20 Saturday

21 Sunday

The Naming of Cats

The Naming of Cats is a difficult matter,
 It isn't just one of your holiday games;
You may think at first I'm as mad as a hatter
When I tell you, a cat must have THREE DIFFERENT NAMES.
First of all, there's the name that the family use daily,
 Such as Peter, Augustus, Alonzo or James,
Such as Victor or Jonathan, George or Bill Bailey –
 All of them sensible everyday names.
There are fancier names if you think they sound sweeter,
 Some for the gentlemen, some for the dames:
Such as Plato, Admetus, Electra, Demeter –
 But all of them sensible everyday names.
But I tell you, a cat needs a name that's particular,
 A name that's peculiar, and more dignified,
Else how can he keep up his tail perpendicular,
 Or spread out his whiskers, or cherish his pride?
Of names of this kind, I can give you a quorum,
 Such as Munkustrap, Quaxo, or Coricopat,
Such as Bombalurina, or else Jellylorum –
 Names that never belong to more than one cat.
But above and beyond there's still one name left over,
 And that is the name that you never will guess;
The name that no human research can discover –
 But THE CAT HIMSELF KNOWS, and will never confess.
When you notice a cat in profound meditation,
 The reason, I tell you, is always the same:
His mind is engaged in a rapt contemplation
 Of the thought, of the thought, of the thought of his name:
 His ineffable effable
 Effanineffable
Deep and inscrutable singular Name.

22 Monday

23 Tuesday

24 Wednesday

25 Thursday

26 Friday

27 Saturday   28 Sunday

The Mower to the Glow-worms

i

Ye living Lamps, by whose dear light
The Nightingale does sit so late,
And studying all the Summer-night,
Her matchless Songs does meditate;

ii

Ye Country Comets, that portend
No War, nor Princes funeral,
Shining unto no higher end
Than to presage the Grasses fall;

iii

Ye Glow-worms, whose officious Flame
To wandring Mowers shows the way,
That in the Night have lost their aim,
And after foolish Fires do stray;

iv

Your courteous Lights in vain you waste,
Since Juliana here is come,
For She my Mind hath so displac'd
That I shall never find my home.

POET TO POET — *Andrew Marvell: Poems selected by Sean O'Brien*

29 Monday   SUMMER BANK HOLIDAY (UK NOT SCT)

30 Tuesday

31 Wednesday

1 Thursday

2 Friday

3 Saturday   4 Sunday

Disintegration

Time running beneath the pillow wakes
Lovers entrained who in the name of love
Were promised the steeples and fanlights of a dream;
Joins the renters of each single room
Across the tables to observe a life
Dissolving in the acid of their sex;

Time that scatters hair upon a head
Spreads the ice sheet on the shaven lawn;
Signing an annual permit for the frost
Ploughs the stubble in the land at last
To introduce the unknown to the known
And only by politeness make them breed;

Time over the roofs of what has nearly been
Circling, a migratory, static bird,
Predicts no change in future's lancing shape,
And daylight shows the streets still tangled up;
Time points the simian camera in the head
Upon confusion to be seen and seen.

5 Monday   LABOUR DAY (NZ)

6 Tuesday

7 Wednesday

8 Thursday

9 Friday

10 Saturday   11 Sunday

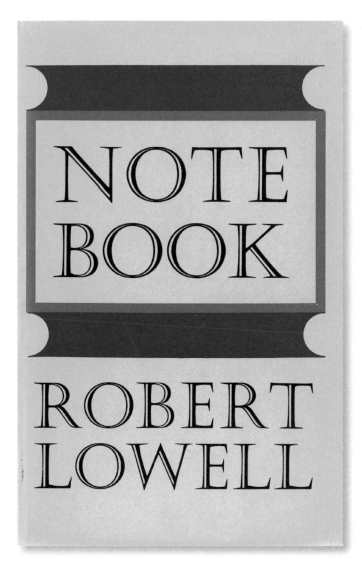

12 Monday

---

13 Tuesday

---

14 Wednesday

---

15 Thursday

---

16 Friday

---

17 Saturday   18 Sunday

'When I have fears that I may cease to be'

When I have fears that I may cease to be
    Before my pen has gleaned my teeming brain,
Before high-pilèd books, in charactery,
    Hold like rich garners the full-ripened grain;
When I behold, upon the night's starred face,
    Huge cloudy symbols of a high romance,
And think that I may never live to trace
    Their shadows, with the magic hand of chance;
And when I feel, fair creature of an hour!
    That I shall never look upon thee more,
Never have relish in the faery power
    Of unreflecting love! – then on the shore
Of the wide world I stand alone, and think
Till love and fame to nothingness do sink.

POET TO POET — *John Keats: Poems selected by Andrew Motion*

19 Monday

20 Tuesday

21 Wednesday

22 Thursday

23 Friday

24 Saturday   HERITAGE DAY (ZA)   25 Sunday

Changes

Birds singing in the rain, in the dawn chorus,
on power lines. Birds knocking on the lawn,
and poor mistaken worms answering them . . .

They take no thought for the morrow, not like you
in your new job. – It paid for my flowers, now
already stricken in years. The stiff cornflowers

bleach, their blue rinse grows out. The marigolds
develop a stoop and go bald, orange clowns,
straw polls, their petals coming out in fistfuls . . .

Hard to take you in your new professional pride –
a salary, place of work, colleagues, corporate spirit –
your new *femme d'affaires* haircut, hard as nails.

Say I must be repressive, afraid of castration,
loving the quest better than its fulfilment.
– What became of you, bright sparrow, featherhead?

26 Monday

27 Tuesday

28 Wednesday

29 Thursday

30 Friday

1 Saturday   2 Sunday

Pied Beauty

Glory be to God for dappled things –
  For skies of couple-colour as a brinded cow;
    For rose-moles all in stipple upon trout that swim;
Fresh-firecoal chestnut-falls; finches' wings;
  Landscape plotted and pieced – fold, fallow, and plough;
    And áll trádes, their gear and tackle and trim.

All things counter, original, spare, strange;
  Whatever is fickle, freckled (who knows how?)
    With swift, slow; sweet, sour; adazzle, dim;
He fathers-forth whose beauty is past change:
               Praise him.

POET TO POET – *Gerard Manley Hopkins: Poems selected by John Stammers*

3 Monday

4 Tuesday

5 Wednesday

6 Thursday

7 Friday

8 Saturday   9 Sunday

Introducing
DAVID
JONES

a selection of his writings
edited by
JOHN MATTHIAS
with a preface by
STEPHEN SPENDER

10 Monday

11 Tuesday

12 Wednesday

13 Thursday

14 Friday

15 Saturday   16 Sunday

Stars and Jasmine

Each of them has been a god many times:
cat, hedgehog and – our summer interloper – the tortoise.
A perfect triangle, they can neither eat
nor marry one another.
And tonight they are gods
under the jasmine under the stars.

Already the hedgehog has scoffed the cat's supper
and she's walked nonplussed beside him
escaping headlong into the bushes.
Wisely now, she keeps an eye on him there,
and on the tortoise
noisily criss-crossing the gravel.

For the cat, jasmine is white
but the stars have colours.
For the hedgehog, there are no stars
only a sky of jasmine,
against which he sniffs something dark,
outlined like a bird of prey.

Wisely, the tortoise ignores both jasmine and stars.
Isn't it enough, she says, to carry the sky on your back,
a sky that is solid, mathematical and delicately coloured –
on which someone, too, has painted
our neighbours' address: 9a Surrey Rd.
Come September, we will lower her through their letterbox.

17 Monday

---

18 Tuesday

---

19 Wednesday

---

20 Thursday

---

21 Friday

---

22 Saturday   23 Sunday

Proud Songsters

The thrushes sing as the sun is going,
And the finches whistle in ones and pairs,
And as it gets dark loud nightingales
    In bushes
Pipe, as they can when April wears,
    As if all Time were theirs.

These are brand new birds of twelve-months' growing,
Which a year ago, or less than twain,
No finches were, nor nightingales,
    Nor thrushes,
But only particles of grain,
    And earth, and air, and rain.

POET TO POET — *Thomas Hardy: Poems selected by Tom Paulin*

24 Monday LABOUR DAY (NZ)

25 Tuesday

26 Wednesday

27 Thursday

28 Friday

29 Saturday   30 Sunday

Some Pike for Nicholas

Down the black drain, and across the Black Lough
Where whitecaps burned, you came tossing on a saucer
Out of childhood, pulled by lean black pike.
From bridle and bit you freed them, and shook hands.

Lough na Cashel's great Queen granted you your prayer
Which was to take her in your arms, on your mother's birthday,
And give her the kiss of life in the cat's tail shallows.
A loon lauded you and an otter saluted.

The pike's broad grin, ruffed with Lough Gur's ice,
Stoniest, oldest eye of reality,
Welcomed your welcome, where crannogs pondered
My boy, my dream alive without distraction.

Through the November, gale-torn, indigo dusk
You fought Lough Allen. It reared, the size of a man,
Shook blood-lit gills and rode a flying serpent . . .
The swipe of that huge tail rocking the memory yet, like a
     hurricane lantern.

31 Monday OCTOBER BANK HOLIDAY (IRL.)

1 Tuesday

2 Wednesday

3 Thursday

4 Friday

5 Saturday 6 Sunday

'What Is She Writing? Perhaps It Will Be Good'

What is she writing? Perhaps it will be good,
The young girl laughs: 'I am in love.'
But the older girl is serious: 'Not now, perhaps later.'
Still the young girl teases: 'What's the matter?
To lose everything! A waste of time!'
But now the older one is quite silent,
Writing, writing, and perhaps it will be good.
Really neither girl is a fool.

7 Monday

8 Tuesday

9 Wednesday

10 Thursday

11 Friday

12 Saturday   13 Sunday REMEMBRANCE SUNDAY

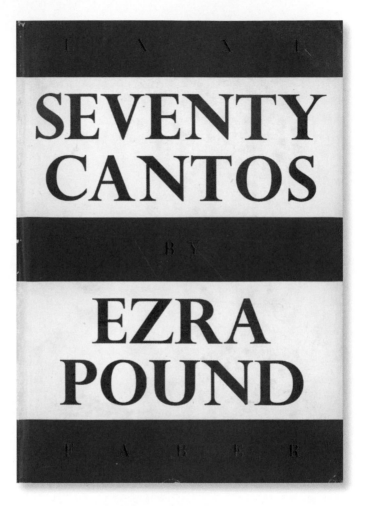

14 Monday

---

15 Tuesday

---

16 Wednesday

---

17 Thursday

---

18 Friday

---

19 Saturday   20 Sunday

Rat, O Rat . . .

never in all my life have I seen
as handsome a rat as you.
Thank you for noticing my potatoes.

O Rat, I am not rich.
I left you a note concerning my potatoes,
but I see that I placed it too high
and you could not read it.

O Rat, my wife and I are cursed
with the possession of a large and hungry dog;
it worries us that he might learn your name —
which is forever on our lips.

O Rat, consider my neighbour:
he has eight children (all of them older
and more intelligent than mine)
and if you lived in his house, Rat,

ten good Christians
(if we include his wife)
would sing your praises nightly,
whereas in my house there are only five.

21 Monday

---

22 Tuesday

---

23 Wednesday

---

24 Thursday

---

25 Friday

---

26 Saturday   27 Sunday

Sometimes your sadness is a yacht

huge, white and expensive, like an anvil
dropped from heaven: how will we get onboard,
up there, when it hurts our necks to look?

Other times it is a rock on the lawn, and matter
can never be destroyed. But today we hold it
to the edge of our bed, shutting our eyes

on another opened hour and listening
to our neighbours' voices having the voices
of their friends around for lunch.

28 Monday

29 Tuesday

30 Wednesday   ST ANDREW'S DAY HOLIDAY (SCT)

1 Thursday

2 Friday

3 Saturday   4 Sunday

In the Valley of Cauteretz

All along the valley, stream that flashest white,
Deepening thy voice with the deepening of the night,
All along the valley, where thy waters flow,
I walked with one I loved two and thirty years ago.
All along the valley, while I walked today,
The two and thirty years were a mist that rolls away;
For all along the valley, down thy rocky bed,
Thy living voice to me was as the voice of the dead,
And all along the valley, by rock and cave and tree,
The voice of the dead was a living voice to me.

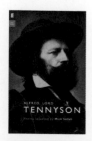

POET TO POET — *Alfred, Lord Tennyson: Poems selected by Mick Imlah*

5 Monday

6 Tuesday

7 Wednesday

8 Thursday

9 Friday

10 Saturday

11 Sunday

SYLVIA PLATH

winter trees

12 Monday

---

13 Tuesday

---

14 Wednesday

---

15 Thursday

---

16 Friday   DAY OF RECONCILIATION (ZA)

---

17 Saturday   18 Sunday

Ice Maiden

I walk in my night-dress and slippers
along winter beaches in Finland.
My earrings of polished tin
flash at the Northern Lights.
I shovel up the sea.

But the cold is quick. Quick
as I crack open the rock
of the ocean with my axe,
it freezes behind me.
My task is endless.

19 Monday

20 Tuesday

21 Wednesday

22 Thursday

23 Friday

24 Saturday   CHRISTMAS EVE   25 Sunday   CHRISTMAS DAY
(UK, IRL, CA, AUS, NZ, ZA)

Stanzas for Music

There be none of Beauty's daughters
    With a magic like thee;
And like music on the waters
    Is thy sweet voice to me:
When, as if its sound were causing
The charmed ocean's pausing,
The waves lie still and gleaming,
And the lulled winds seem dreaming.

And the midnight moon is weaving
    Her bright chain o'er the deep;
Whose breast is gently heaving,
    As an infant's asleep.
So the spirit bows before thee,
To listen and adore thee,
With a full but soft emotion,
Like the swell of Summer's ocean.

POET TO POET — *Lord Byron: Poems selected by Paul Muldoon*

26 Monday BOXING DAY (UK, AUS, NZ)

ST STEPHEN'S DAY (IRL) DAY OF GOODWILL (ZA)

27 Tuesday BANK HOLIDAY (UK, AUS, NZ)

28 Wednesday

29 Thursday

30 Friday

31 Saturday NEW YEAR'S EVE   1 Sunday NEW YEAR'S DAY

(UK, IRL, AUS, NZ, ZA)

A Brief Chronology of Faber's Poetry Publishing

1925 Geoffrey Faber acquires an interest in The Scientific Press and renames the firm Faber and Gwyer. ¶ The poet/bank clerk T. S. Eliot is recruited. 'What will impress my directors favourably is the sense that in you we have found a man who combines literary gifts with business instincts.' – Geoffrey Faber to T. S. Eliot ¶ Eliot brought with him *The Criterion*, the quarterly periodical he had been editing since 1922. (*The Waste Land* had appeared in its first issue, brilliantly establishing its reputation.) He continued to edit it from the Faber offices until it closed in 1939. Though unprofitable it was hugely influential, introducing early work by Auden, Empson and Spender, amongst others, and promoting many notable European writers, including Proust and Valéry. ¶ Publication of T. S. Eliot's *Poems, 1909–1925*, which included *The Waste Land* and a new sequence, *The Hollow Men*. ¶

1927 From 1927 to 1931 Faber publishes a series of illustrated pamphlets known as *The Ariel Poems* containing unpublished poems by an eminent poet (Thomas Hardy, W. B. Yeats, Harold Monro, Edith Sitwell and Edmund Blunden to name but a few) along with an illustration, usually in colour, by a leading contemporary artist (including Eric Gill, Eric Ravilious, Paul Nash and Graham Sutherland). ¶

1928 Faber and Gwyer announce the *Selected Poems of Ezra Pound*, with an introduction and notes by Eliot. ¶

1929 Geoffrey Faber buys out Lady Gwyer and oversees the birth of the Faber and Faber imprint. Legend has it that Walter de la Mare, the father of Faber director Richard de la Mare, suggested the euphonious repetition: another Faber in the company name 'because you can't have too much of a good thing'. ¶

1930 W. H. Auden becomes a Faber poet with a collection entitled simply *Poems*. ¶ Eliot publishes *Ash Wednesday*. ¶

1933 Stephen Spender becomes a Faber poet with his first collection *Poems*, a companion piece to Auden's 1930 work of the same name. ¶ The first British edition of James Joyce's *Pomes Penyeach* is published. ¶

1935 The American poet Marianne Moore publishes with Faber. 'Miss Moore's poems form part of a small body of durable poetry written in our time.' – T. S. Eliot ¶ Louis MacNeice becomes a Faber poet. 'The most original Irish poet of his generation.' – Faber catalogue 1935 ¶

1936 The hugely influential *Faber Book of Modern Verse* (edited by Michael Roberts) is published. ¶

1937 *In Parenthesis* by David Jones is published. 'This is an epic of war. But it is like no other war-book because for the first time that experience has been reduced to "a shape in words." The impression still remains that this book is one of the most remarkable literary achievements of our time.' – *Times Literary Supplement* ¶ W. H. Auden is awarded the Queen's Gold Medal for Poetry. ¶

1939 T. S. Eliot's *Old Possum's Book of Practical Cats* is published with a book jacket illustrated by the author. Originally called *Pollicle Dogs and Jellicle Cats*, the poems were written for his five godchildren. The eldest of these was Geoffrey Faber's son Tom – himself much later a director of Faber and Faber. ¶

1944 Walter de la Mare's *Peacock Pie* is published with illustrations by Edward Ardizzone. ¶ Philip Larkin's first novel, *A Girl in Winter*, is published. 'A young man with an exceptionally clear sense of what, as a writer, he means to do.' – *Times Literary Supplement* ¶

1948 T. S. Eliot wins the Nobel Prize in Literature. ¶

1949 Ezra Pound's *Pisan Cantos* is published. 'The most incomprehensible passages are often more stimulating than much comprehensibility which passes for poetry today.' – *Times Literary Supplement* ¶

1954 *The Ariel Poems* are revived with a new set of pamphlets by W. H. Auden, Stephen Spender, Louis MacNeice, T. S. Eliot, Walter de la Mare, Cecil Day Lewis and Roy Campbell. The artists include Edward Ardizzone, Edward Bawden, Michael Ayrton and John Piper. ¶

1957 Ted Hughes comes to Faber with *The Hawk in the Rain*. ¶ Siegfried Sassoon receives the Queen's Gold Medal for Poetry. ¶

1959 Robert Lowell's collection *Life Studies* is published. ¶

1960 Saint-John Perse wins the Nobel Prize in Literature.

1961 Geoffrey Faber dies. ¶ Ted Hughes's first collection of children's poems, *Meet My Folks*, is published. ¶

1963 Sylvia Plath's novel *The Bell Jar* is published by Faber in the year of her death. ¶ The Geoffrey Faber Memorial Prize is established as an annual prize awarded in alternating years to a single volume of poetry or fiction by a Commonwealth author under forty. ¶

1964 Philip Larkin's *The Whitsun Weddings* is published. ¶

1965 T. S. Eliot dies. ¶ Sylvia Plath's posthumous collection, *Ariel*, is published. 'Her extraordinary achievement, poised as she was between volatile emotional state and the edge of the precipice.' – Frieda Hughes ¶ Philip Larkin is awarded the Queen's Gold Medal for Poetry. ¶

1966 Seamus Heaney comes to Faber with *Death of a Naturalist*. ¶

1968 Ted Hughes's *The Iron Man* is published. ¶

1971 Stephen Spender is awarded the Queen's Gold Medal for Poetry. ¶

1973 Paul Muldoon comes to Faber with his first collection, *New Weather*. ¶

1974 Ted Hughes receives the Queen's Gold Medal for Poetry. ¶

1977 Tom Paulin comes to Faber with his first collection, *A State of Justice*. ¶ Norman Nicholson receives the Queen's Gold Medal for Poetry. ¶

1980 Csezlaw Milosz wins the Nobel Prize in Literature. ¶

1981 *Cats*, the Andrew Lloyd Webber musical based on *Old Possum's Book of Practical Cats*, opens in London. ¶

1984 *Rich*, a collection by Faber's own poetry editor, Craig Raine, is published. 'Puts us in touch with life as unexpectedly and joyfully as early Pasternak.' – John Bayley ¶ Ted Hughes becomes Poet Laureate. ¶

1985 Douglas Dunn's collection *Elegies* is the Whitbread Book of the Year. ¶

1986 Vikram Seth's *The Golden Gate* is published. ¶

1987 Seamus Heaney's *The Haw Lantern* wins the Whitbread Prize for Poetry. ¶

1988 Derek Walcott is awarded the Queen's Gold Medal for Poetry. ¶

1992 Derek Walcott wins the Nobel Prize in Literature. ¶ Thom Gunn's collection *The Man with the Night Sweats* wins the Forward Poetry Prize for Best Collection, while Simon Armitage's *Kid* wins Best First Collection. ¶

1993 Andrew Motion wins the Whitbread Prize for Biography for his book on Philip Larkin. ¶ Don Paterson's *Nil Nil* wins the Forward Poetry Prize for Best First Collection. ¶

1994 Paul Muldoon wins the T. S. Eliot Prize for *The Annals of Chile*. ¶ Alice Oswald wins an Eric Gregory Award. ¶

1995 Seamus Heaney wins the Nobel Prize in Literature. ¶

1996 Wislawa Szymborska wins the Nobel Prize in Literature. ¶ Seamus Heaney's *The Spirit Level* wins the Whitbread Prize for Poetry. 'Touched by a sense of wonder.' – Blake Morrison ¶

1997 Don Paterson wins the T. S. Eliot Prize for *God's Gift to Women*. ¶ Lavinia Greenlaw wins the Forward Prize for Best Single Poem for 'A World Where News Travelled Slowly'. ¶ Ted Hughes's *Tales from Ovid* is the Whitbread Book of the Year. 'A breathtaking book.' – John Carey ¶

1998 Ted Hughes wins the Whitbread Book of the Year for the second time running with *Birthday Letters*, which also wins the T. S. Eliot Prize. 'Language like lava, its molten turmoils hardening into jagged shapes.' – John Carey ¶ Ted Hughes is awarded the Order of Merit. ¶ Christopher Logue receives the Wilfred Owen Poetry Award. ¶

1999 Seamus Heaney's *Beowulf* wins the Whitbread Book of the Year Award. '[Heaney is the] one living poet who can rightly claim to be Beowulf's heir.' – *New York Times* ¶ A memorial service for Ted Hughes is held at Westminster Abbey. In his speech Seamus Heaney calls Hughes 'a guardian spirit of the land and language'. ¶ Hugo Williams wins the T. S. Eliot Prize for his collection *Billy's Rain*. ¶ Andrew Motion is appointed Poet Laureate. ¶

2000 Seamus Heaney receives the Wilfred Owen Poetry Award. ¶

2002 Alice Oswald wins the T. S. Eliot Prize for Poetry for her collection *Dart*. ¶

2003 Paul Muldoon is awarded the Pulitzer Prize for Poetry for *Moy Sand and Gravel*. ¶

2004 August Kleinzahler receives the International Griffin Prize for *The Strange Hours Travellers Keep*. ¶ Hugo Williams is awarded the Queen's Gold Medal for Poetry. ¶

2005 David Harsent wins the Forward Prize for Best Collection for *Legion*. ¶ Harold Pinter receives the Wilfred Owen Poetry Award. ¶ Charles Simic receives the International Griffin Prize for *Selected Poems 1963– 2003*. ¶ Nick Laird wins an Eric Gregory Award. ¶

2006 Christopher Logue wins the Whitbread Prize for Poetry for *Cold Calls*. ¶ The Geoffrey Faber Memorial Prize is awarded to Alice Oswald for *Woods Etc*. ¶ Seamus Heaney wins the T. S. Eliot Prize for *District and Circle*. ¶

2007 Tony Harrison is awarded the Wilfred Owen Award for Poetry. ¶ Daljit Nagra wins the Forward Prize for Best First Collection for *Look We Have Coming to Dover!* ¶ James Fenton receives the Queen's Gold Medal for Poetry. ¶

2008 Daljit Nagra wins the South Bank Show/Arts Council Decibel Award. ¶ Mick Imlah's collection *The Lost Leader* wins the Forward Prize for Best Collection. ¶

2009 Carol Ann Duffy becomes Poet Laureate. ¶ Don Paterson's *Rain* wins the Forward Poetry Prize for Best Collection while *The Striped World* by Emma Jones wins the Best First Collection Prize. ¶

2010 *The Song of Lunch* by Christopher Reid is shortlisted for the Ted Hughes Award for New Work in Poetry and he is awarded the Costa Book Prize for *A Scattering*. ¶ The John Florio Prize for Italian Translation 2010 is awarded to Jamie McKendrick for *The Embrace*. ¶ Derek Walcott wins both the Warwick Prize and the T. S. Eliot Prize for Poetry for his collection *White Egrets*. ¶ *Rain* by Don Paterson is shortlisted for the Saltire Scottish Book of the Year. ¶ Tony Harrison is awarded the Prix Européen de Litérature. ¶ The Keats–Shelley Prize is awarded to Simon Armitage for his poem *The Present*. ¶ The Forward Prize for Best Collection is awarded to Seamus Heaney for *Human Chain*. ¶ Also shortlisted for the Forward Prize for Best Collection are Lachlan Mackinnon for *Small Hours* and Jo Shapcott for *Of Mutability*. ¶ The Centre for Literacy in Primary Education (CLPE) Poetry Prize is awarded to Carol Ann Duffy for *New and Collected Poems for Children*. ¶ Alice Oswald wins the Ted Hughes Award for New Work in Poetry for *Weeds and Wild Flowers*. ¶ *The Striped World* by Emma Jones is shortlisted for the Adelaide Festival Poetry Award. ¶ The Queen's Medal for Poetry is awarded to Don Paterson. ¶

2011 *Of Mutability* by Jo Shapcott is the Costa Book of the Year. ¶ *Human Chain* by Seamus Heaney and *Maggot* by Paul Muldoon are both shortlisted for the *Irish Times* Poetry Now Award. ¶ *Night* by David Harsent is shortlisted for the Forward Prize for Best Collection. ¶ 'Bees' by Jo Shapcott is shortlisted for the Forward Prize for Best Poem. ¶ A new digital edition of T. S. Eliot's *The Waste Land* for iPad is launched, bringing to life one of the most revolutionary poems of the last hundred years, illuminated by a wealth of interactive features. ¶ The Queen's Gold Medal for Poetry is awarded to Jo Shapcott. ¶ At Westminster Abbey a memorial is dedicated to Ted Hughes in Poets' Corner. ¶

2012 *The Death of King Arthur* by Simon Armitage is shortlisted for the T. S. Eliot Prize. ¶ *The World's Two Smallest Humans* by Julia Copus is shortlisted for the T. S. Eliot Prize and the Costa Book Award. ¶ David Harsent's collection *Night* wins the 2012 International Griffin Poetry Prize. ¶ *81 Austerities* by Sam Riviere wins the Felix Dennis Prize for Best First Collection, one of the Forward Prizes for Poetry. ¶ *Farmers Cross* by Bernard O'Donoghue is shortlisted for the Irish Times Poetry Now Award. ¶

2013 The Forward Prize for Best First Collection is awarded to Emily Berry for *Dear Boy*. ¶ Hugo Williams is shortlisted for the Forward Prize for Best Single

Poem for 'From the Dialysis Ward'. ¶ Alice Oswald is awarded the Warwick Prize for Writing for her collection *Memorial*, which also wins the Poetry Society's Corneliu M. Popescu Prize for poetry in translation. ¶ The Queen's Gold Medal for Poetry is awarded to Douglas Dunn. ¶ The shortlist for the 2013 T. S. Eliot Prize includes Daljit Nagra for *The Ramayana: A Retelling* and Maurice Riordan for *The Water Stealer*. ¶ *Pink Mist* by Owen Sheers wins the Hay Festival Medal for Poetry. ¶ In his eulogy for Seamus Heaney, Paul Muldoon says, 'We remember the beauty of Seamus Heaney – as a bard, and in his being.' In November the first official tribute evenings to Heaney are held at Harvard, then in New York, followed by events at the Royal Festival Hall in London, the Waterfront Hall, Belfast, and the Sheldonian, Oxford. ¶

2014 Maurice Riordan is shortlisted for the Pigott Poetry Prize for *The Water Stealer*. ¶ Hugo Williams is shortlisted for the Forward Prize for Best Collection for *I Knew the Bride*. ¶ Daljit Nagra is awarded the Society of Authors Travelling Scholarship. ¶ Nick Laird's *Go Giants* is shortlisted for the *Irish Times* Poetry Now Award. ¶ Emily Berry, Emma Jones and Daljit Nagra are announced as three of the Poetry Book Society's Next Generation Poets 2014. ¶ *Pink Mist* by Owen Sheers is named the Wales Book of the Year after winning the poetry category.

Acknowledgements

Poetry

All poetry reprinted by permission of Faber & Faber unless otherwise stated.

'Glanmore Sonnets VII' taken from *New Selected Poems 1966–1987* © Estate of Seamus Heaney

'Morning Song' taken from *Collected Poems* © Estate of Sylvia Plath

'Tomato Salad' taken from *Dear Boy* © Emily Berry

'Heronkind' taken from *The World's Two Smallest Humans* © Julia Copus

'Religion' taken from *West End Final* © Hugo Williams

'Teazles' taken from *Out There* © Jamie McKendrick

'Modern Love' taken from *New Selected Poems 1964–2000* © Douglas Dunn

'If I Could Tell You' © 1945 by W. H. Auden, reprinted by permission of Curtis Brown, Ltd

'Year of the Rabbit' taken from *81 Austerities* © Sam Riviere

'The Strand' taken from *Collected Poems* © Estate of Louis MacNeice

'Canute' taken from *Small Hours* © Lachlan Mackinnon

'I Leave This at Your Ear' taken from *New Collected Poems* © Estate of W. S. Graham

'The Day I Outlived My Father' from *Outliving* © Bernard O'Donoghue, published by Chatto & Windus. Reprinted by permission of the Random House Group Limited

'Hinterhof' taken from *Yellow Tulips* © James Fenton

'The Naming of Cats' taken from *The Complete Poems & Plays* © Estate of T. S. Eliot

'Disintegration' taken from *The Complete Poems* © Estate of Philip Larkin

'Changes' taken from *Selected Poems* © Michael Hofmann

'Stars and Jasmine' taken from *The Water Stealer* © Maurice Riordan

'Some Pike for Nicholas' taken from *Collected Poems* © Estate of Ted Hughes

'What Is She Writing? Perhaps It Will Be Good' taken from *Collected Poems and Drawings of Stevie Smith* © Estate of Stevie Smith

'Rat, O Rat' taken from *Selected Poems* © Estate of Christopher Logue

'Sometimes Your Sadness Is a Yacht' taken from *Happiness* © Jack Underwood

'Ice Maiden' taken from *Hare Soup* © Dorothy Molloy

Picture Credits

All jacket designs by Berthold Wolpe except for: *Station Island* by Pentagram, *Winter Trees* by Shirley Tucker, and *Seventy Cantos* and *Notebook* by Faber & Faber.

NOTES

Faber Members is a free-to-join programme from one of the world's great publishers. Sign up now for discounts on Faber books and Faber Academy courses as well as exclusive access to a range of hand-bound Collectors' Editions.

FABER ACADEMY
—*creative writing courses with character*—

faberacademy.co.uk/**courses**

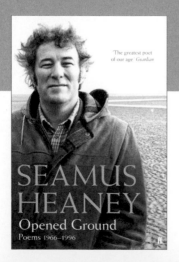

Simon Armitage Book of Matches

Poetry ff

Simon Armitage Seeing Stars

Poetry ff

W. H. Auden The Dyer's Hand

ff

W. H. Auden Selected Poems

Revised Edition
Edited by Edward Mende

Poetry

Mark Ford Soft Sift

Poetry ff

Matthew Francis Muscovy

Poetry ff

Lavinia Greenlaw The Casual Perfect

Poetry ff

Ian Hamilto Collecte Poems

Edited by Alan Jenkins

Poetry

James Joyce Poems and Shorter Writings

Edited by Richard Ellmann
A. Walton Litz and
John Whittier-Ferguson

Poetry ff

Nick Laird Go Giants

Poetry ff

Logue's Homer Cold Calls
War Music continued

Poetry ff

Andrew Motion The Cinder Path

Poetry ff

Don Paterson Selected Poems

Poetry ff

Sylvia Plath Ariel

Poetry ff

Ezra Pound Selected Poems 1908–1969

Poetry ff

Christophe Reid Nonsense

Poetry